In a Dark, Dark Wood

A Traditional Tale

In a dark, dark wood,

2

there was a dark, dark path.

And up that dark, dark path,

4

there was a dark, dark house.

And in that dark, dark house,

there was a dark, dark stair.

And up that dark, dark stair,

8

there was a dark, dark room.

And in that dark, dark room,

there was
a dark, dark cupboard.

And in
that dark, dark cupboard,

there was a dark, dark box.

And in that dark, dark box,

14

there was a